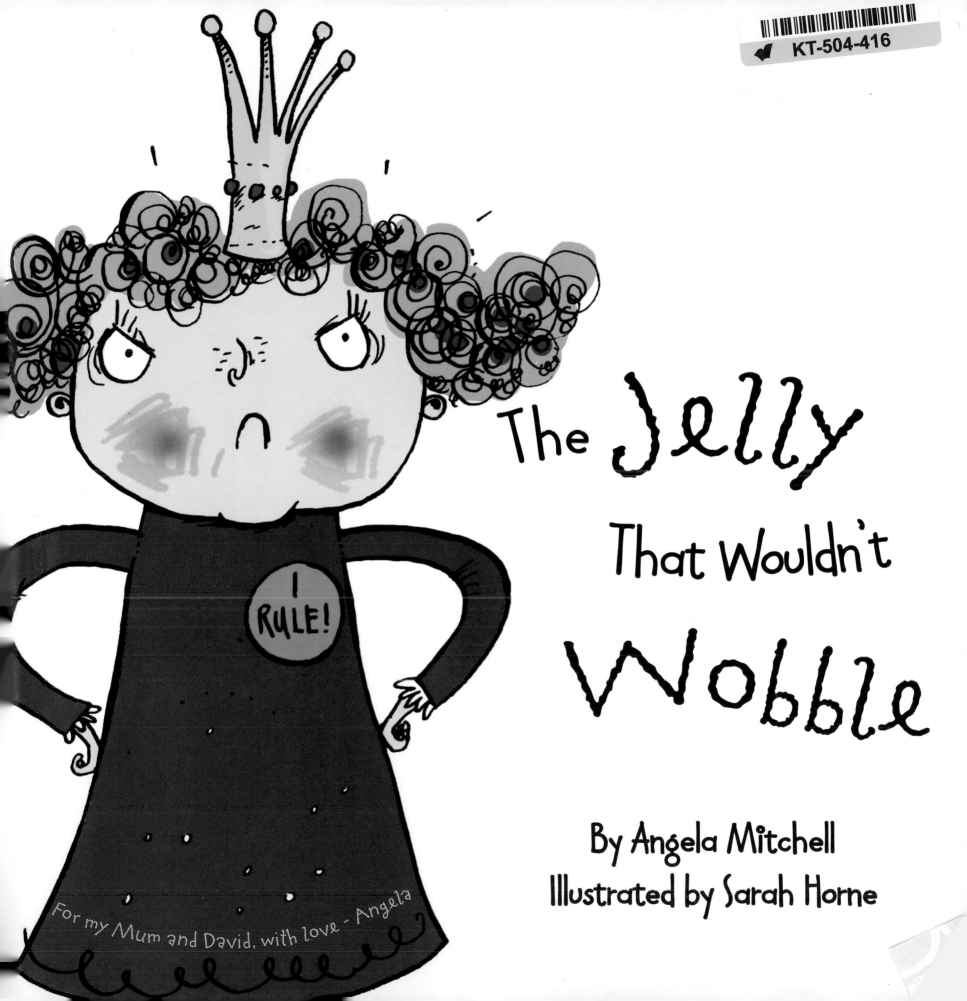

I RULE!

The Jelly That Wouldn't Wobble

For my Mum and David, with love - Angela

By Angela Mitchell

Illustrated by Sarah Horne

Princess Lolly wriggled impatiently on her throne. It was her 89th birthday party.

"Where's my special jelly?" she asked.

"Here, Your Highness!" replied the guard, as the cook and his assistant proudly carried in her special jelly.

Everyone gasped with delight.

It was GLORIOUS!

Princess Lolly squealed with excitement, prodded the jelly and then looked puzzled. She prodded the jelly again...

"This jelly doesn't wobble!" exclaimed Princess Lolly in horror. The cook prodded the jelly too.

"Doesn't wobble?
Doesn't wobble?"
flustered the cook.
"Of course it wobbles,
Your Highness: it's jelly!"

"I. SAY. THIS. JELLY. DOESN'T. WOBBLE!"
screeched the Princess hysterically.
She prodded the jelly again and again...
and again. It didn't wobble!

"I want my jelly to wobble!
Make it wobble!
WHY. WON'T. MY.
JELLY. WOBBLE?"
she stomped, a royal tear
rolling down her cheek.

Everyone looked at the
jelly in wonder.

Princess Lolly slumped on her throne, the cook stared in disbelief, the guard stood to attention and the hungry guests sat back in silence.

"Not be eaten?" boomed the Princess.

"MELT IT!"

"Your Highness, NO!" begged the cook.
"Think of the mess, Your Highness," said the guard.
Princess Lolly pondered for a moment.

"A thousand and one chocolate sovereigns for anyone who can make this jelly wobble!" announced the Princess.

There was a great stir...

"I'll prod it with my walking stick!" said the oldest guest.

That didn't work.

"Rock the table!" shouted the twin guests.

That didn't work.

"Scare it!" the royal window cleaner hollered and pulled some horrible faces.

That didn't work.

The jelly *still* refused to wobble.

"I WON'T WOBBLE! I WON'T WOBBLE AND THAT'S MY FINAL WORD!" screamed the jelly.

Princess Lolly turned the colour of a very ripe strawberry.
The cook turned white with worry.

"I know how to make it wobble,"
said the smallest guest.

"You do?" boomed the Princess.

"You do?" questioned the cook.

"You do?" repeated the cook's assistant.

"Yes, Your Highness," said the smallest guest proudly. "Make the jelly *really, really, really* cold; it will shiver and have to wobble!"

"Wonderful!" said the cook, excited.

"Go on. Go on, I say!" Princess Lolly commanded.
The cook froze for a moment.

"Ice cream, ice cream," whispered the smallest guest to the cook.

"Of course!" gasped the cook.

There was a great scurry while a rather wobbly,
old ladder and the royal ice cream scoop were fetched.

Tottering on the top of the ladder, the cook
placed three scoops of tutti frutti ice cream
on top of the jelly's crown.

Everyone held their breath, and watched as the jelly
tried very hard not to shiver...

Suddenly, the jelly jerked, as the ice cream began to melt and trickle down its sides.

"I saw something move!" gasped the smallest guest.

"Oh, please wobble," begged the cook.

"Brrrrrrr!" The jelly suddenly shivered.

"Brrrrrrrrrrrrrrrrrrrr!"
It shivered again,

What a spectacle!
The guests moved back in fear,
the cook began to cry, and
Princess Lolly stared in wonder at
this quivering, shivering sight as
the defeated jelly...

WOBBLED and WIBBLED, WIBBLED and WOBBLED, just as a royal jelly should!

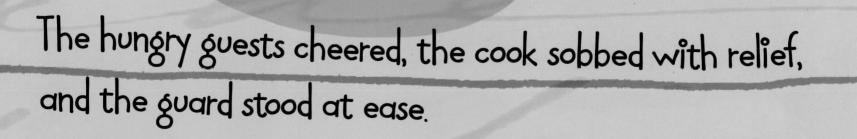

The hungry guests cheered, the cook sobbed with relief, and the guard stood at ease.

"SILENCE!" cried Princess Lolly. There was an instant hush.

"Now we can eat jelly!" she proclaimed.
"Phew," sighed the cook, consoled.

And they did.

(And, by the way, the Princess kept her promise and rewarded the smallest guest with a thousand and one chocolate sovereigns).

THE END

The Jelly That Wouldn't Wobble
An original concept by author Angela Mitchell
© Angela Mitchell
Illustrated by Sarah Horne

Published by MAVERICK ARTS PUBLISHING LTD
Studio 3A, City Business Centre, 6 Brighton Road, Horsham, West Sussex, RH13 5BB
© Maverick Arts Publishing Limited 2014 +44 (0) 1403 256941

A CIP catalogue record for this book is available at the British Library.

ISBN 978-1-84886-079-7

Maverick
arts publishing
www.maverickbooks.co.uk

**THIS EDITION PUBLISHED
2014 FOR INDEX BOOKS**